with the beatles

Exclusive Distributors:
Music Sales Limited
8/9 Frith Street,
London W1V 5TZ, England.
Music Sales Pty Limited
120 Rothschild Avenue,
Rosebery, NSW 2018,
Australia.

This book © Copyright 1992 by Wise Publications
Order No.NO90543
ISBN 0-7119-3267-0

Music arranged by Frank Booth
Music processed by MSS Studios
Book design by Pearce Marchbank Studio
Computer origination by Adam Hay

Unauthorised reproduction of any part of
this publication by any means including
photocopying is an infringement of copyright.

Music Sales' complete catalogue lists thousands of titles
and is free from your local music shop, or direct from
Music Sales Limited. Please send a cheque/postal order
for £1.50 for postage to: Music Sales Limited,
Newmarket Road, Bury St. Edmunds, Suffolk IP33 3YB.

Your Guarantee of Quality
As publishers, we strive to produce every book to the
highest commercial standards.
The music has been freshly engraved and the book has
been carefully designed to minimise awkward page turns
and to make playing from it a real pleasure.
Particular care has been given to specifying acid-free,
neutral-sized paper which has not been chlorine bleached
but produced with special regard for the environment.
Throughout, the printing and binding have been planned
to ensure a sturdy, attractive publication which should
give years of enjoyment.
If your copy fails to meet our high standards,
please inform us and we will gladly replace it.

Printed in the United Kingdom by
Halstan & Co Limited, Amersham, Buckinghamshire.

Wise Publications
London/New York/Sydney/Paris

It Won't Be Long

Words & Music by John Lennon & Paul McCartney.
© Copyright 1963 Northern Songs, under license to
MCA Music Limited, 77 Fulham Palace Road, London W6.
All Rights Reserved. International Copyright Secured.

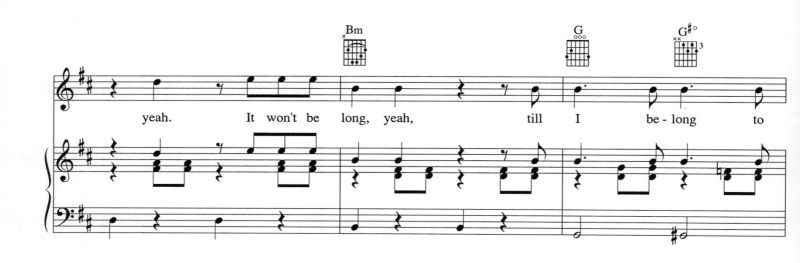

4

All I've Got To Do

Words & Music by John Lennon & Paul McCartney.

© Copyright 1963 Northern Songs, under license to
MCA Music Limited, 77 Fulham Palace Road, London W6.
All Rights Reserved. International Copyright Secured.

that's all I _____ got-ta do. ___   2. And when

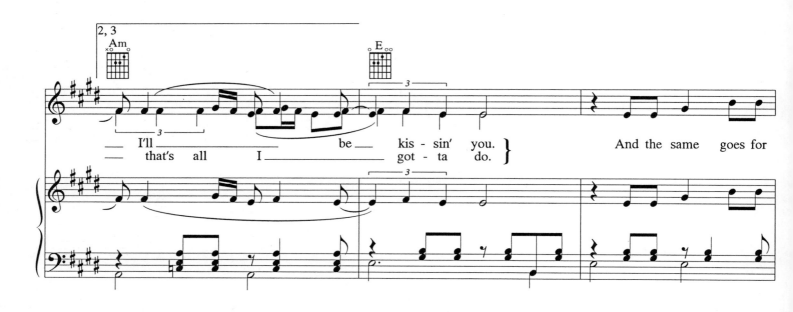

I'll _____ be ___ kis-sin' you.
that's all I _____ got-ta do. }   And the same goes for

me when-ev-er you want me at all, ___ I'll be here, yes I will, when-ev-er you call; ___ You

All My Loving

Words & Music by John Lennon & Paul McCartney.
© Copyright 1963 Northern Songs, under license to
MCA Music Limited, 77 Fulham Palace Road, London W6.
All Rights Reserved. International Copyright Secured.

D.S. al Coda

Tacet

3. Close your

Coda

All my lov-ing, _____ all _____ my lov-ing, ___

oo ___ all my lov-ing _____ I will send to you. _____

Little Child

Words & Music by John Lennon & Paul McCartney.
© Copyright 1963 Northern Songs, under license to
MCA Music Limited, 77 Fulham Palace Road, London W6.
All Rights Reserved. International Copyright Secured.

Ba - by take a chance with me. ___ Lit - tle child, _ Ba - by take a chance with me. ___

___ If you want some - one to make you feel so fine ___ then we'll
by my side you're the on - ly one, ___ don't you

have some fun when you're mine, all mine. ___ So, come on, come on, ___ come
run and hide, just come on, come on. ___ Yeah, come on, come on, ___ come

Don't Bother Me

Words & Music by George Harrison.

© Copyright 1963 Dick James Music Limited, I Sussex Place, London W6.
All Rights Reserved. International Copyright Secured.

Moderate Rock

Tacet

Since she's been gone

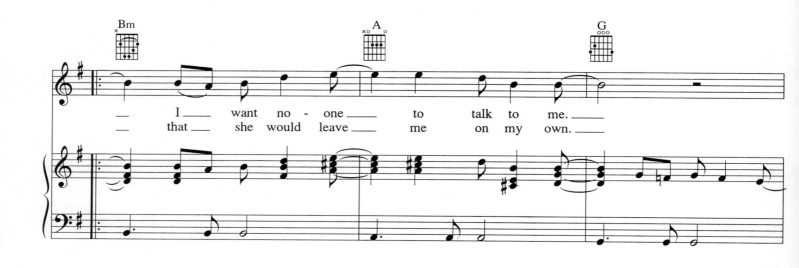

I ____ want no - one ____ to talk to me.
that ____ she would leave ____ me on my own.

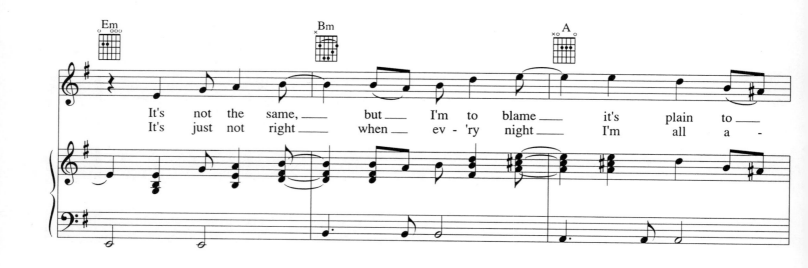

It's not the same, ____ but ____ I'm to blame ____ it's plain to ____
It's just not right ____ when ____ ev - 'ry night ____ I'm all a -

al - ways — be   The on - ly

girl   for   me.   But till she's here — please — don't come near, —

— just stay a - way, —   I'll let you know — when — she's come home. —

— Un - til that — day,   don't come a - round, —

Please Mr Postman

Words & Music by B. Holland & F.C. Gorman.

© Copyright 1962 Jobete Music Company, USA.
Dominion Music Limited, 127 Charing Cross Road, London WC2.
All Rights Reserved. International Copyright Secured.

long, long time ___ Since I heard from that girl of mine. ___

wost - man, ___ oh ___ yeah. ___
wost - man, ___ oh ___ yeah. ___

There must ___ be some word to - day ___ From my girl - friend
So man - y days ___ you've passed me by, ___ See the tears stand - in'

so far a - way. ___ Please Mis - ter Post - man, look and see ___
in my eyes. ___ You did - n't stop to make me feel bet - ter ___

Oh yeah, __ {you got-ta wait a min-ute, wait __ a min-ute, oh yeah. __
Mis-ter Po - wo - wost-man, __ oh yeah. __ De
you got-ta wait a min-ute, wait __ a min-ute, oh yeah. __ Got-ta

Check it and see __ one more time for me. __ You got-ta liv-er the let-ter, the

Repeat and Fade

soon-er the bet __ you got-ta wait a min-ute, wait a min-ute, oh yeah. __ You got-ta

Roll Over Beethoven

Words & Music by Chuck Berry.

© Copyright 1956 Arc Music Corporation, USA.
Jewel Music Publishing Company Limited, 129 Park Street, London W1.
All Rights Reserved. International Copyright Secured.

I'm gon-na write a lit-tle let-ter, gon-na mail it to my lo-cal D. J.

Roll o - ver Bee - tho - ven and tell Tchai - kov - sky the news..

I've got a rock - in' pneu - mo - nia, I need a shot of rhy - thm and blues.

Oo_____ I think I caught an arth - er - i - tis sit - tin' down by the rhy - thm re - views.

Roll o - ver Bee - tho - ven, a - rock - in' in two___ by two.___

29

Well, ear-ly in the morn-in' I'm a giv-in' you the warn-in' don't you step on my blue ___ suede shoes! ___ Hey ___

did-dle, did-dle, I'm a - play my fid-dle, ain't got noth-in' to lose. ___ Roll o -

ver Bee-tho - ven and tell Tchai-kov - sky the news. ___ You know she

wigs like a glow __ worm, danc' like a __ spin-ning top. ___ She's got a

cra-zy part - ner, ought ___ to see 'm reel and rock. ___ Long as she's __

I Wanna Be Your Man

Words & Music by John Lennon & Paul McCartney.
© Copyright 1964 Northern Songs, under license to
MCA Music Limited, 77 Fulham Palace Road, London W6.
All Rights Reserved. International Copyright Secured.

Moderately

1.3. I wan-na be your lov-er, ba - by,
2. Tell me that you love me, ba - by,

I wan-na be your man. ___ I wan-na be your
Let me un-der-stand. ___ Tell me that you

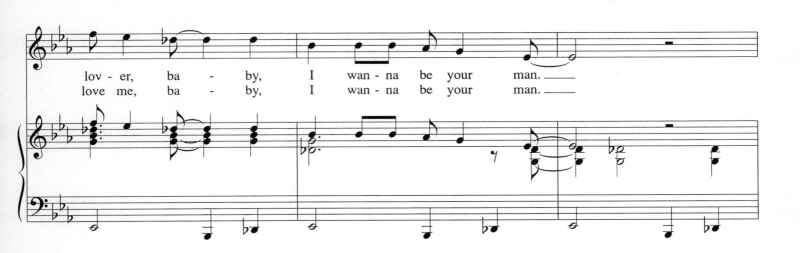

lov-er, ba - by, I wan-na be your man. ___
love me, ba - by, I wan-na be your man. ___

Love you like no oth - er, ba - by, Like no oth - er can. ___
I wan - na be your lov - er, ba - by, I wan - na be your man. ___

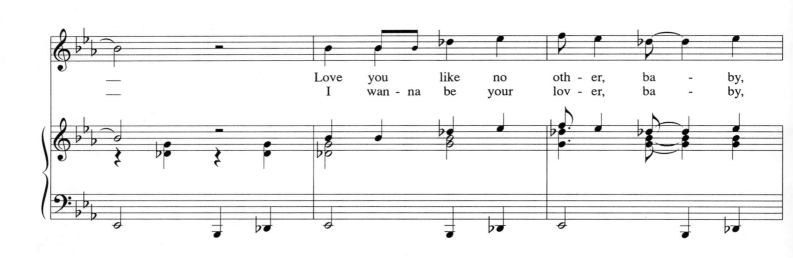

___ Love you like no oth - er, ba - by,
___ I wan - na be your lov - er, ba - by,

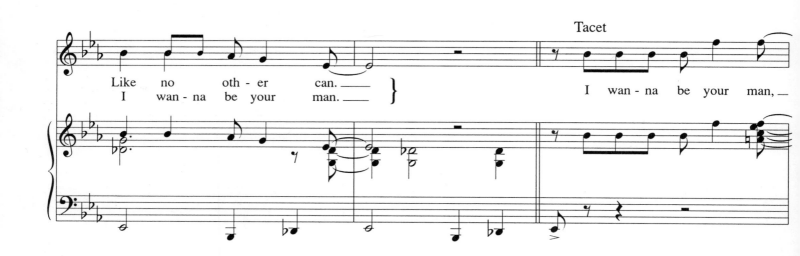

Like no oth - er can. ___
I wan - na be your man. ___

Tacet

I wan - na be your man, ___

I wan - na be your man, ___

I wan - na be your man, ___

I wan - na be your man. ___

Repeat and Fade

I wan - na be your man. ___

Hold Me Tight

Words & Music by John Lennon & Paul McCartney.

© Copyright 1963 Northern Songs, under license to
MCA Music Limited, 77 Fulham Palace Road, London W6.
All Rights Reserved. International Copyright Secured.

hold you tight; ___ Be-ing here a-lone to-night ___ with you, ___

It feels so right { Now hold me tight ___
{ So hold me tight ___

___ Tell me I'm the on-ly one, ___ and
___ Let me go on lov-ing you, ___ to-

then I might ___
-night, to-night, ___ Nev-er be the
Mak-ing love to

You Really Gotta Hold On Me

Words & Music by William Robinson.
© Copyright 1962, 1963 Jobete Music Company Incorporated, USA.
Dominion Music Limited, 127 Charing Cross Road, London WC2.
All Rights Reserved. International Copyright Secured.

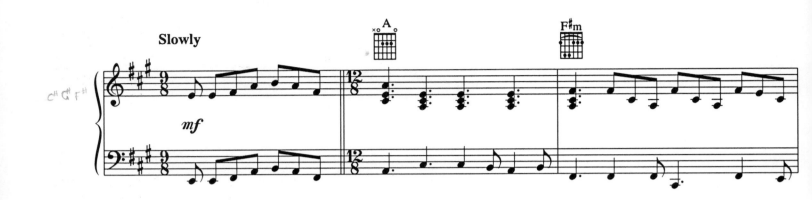

(1) I don't ____ like you, ____
(2) I don't ____ want you, ____
(3) I wan - na leave you, ____

but I ____ love you; Seems that I'm al - ways ____
but I ____ need you; Don't wan - na kiss you, ____
don't wan - na stay here; Don't wan - na spend ____

43

Devil In Her Heart

Words & Music by Richard B. Drapkin.

© Copyright 1962 Slow Dancing Music Incorporated, USA.
MCA Music Limited, 77 Fulham Palace Road, London W6.
All Rights Reserved. International Copyright Secured.

She's got the dev-il in her heart, _____ but her eyes, they tan-ta-

lize. _____ She's gon-na tear your heart a-part, _____

oh, her lips, they real-ly thrill _____ me.

47

Not A Second Time

Words & Music by John Lennon & Paul McCartney.
© Copyright 1963 Northern Songs, under license to
MCA Music Limited, 77 Fulham Palace Road, London W6.
All Rights Reserved. International Copyright Secured.

mind _____ I see no reas-on to change mine; _____ I

cried, _____ it's through. _____ oh, _____

You're giv-ing me the same old ___ line, ___ I'm won-d'ring

why.   You hurt me then,   you're back a-gain;

Money

Words & Music by Berry Gordy Junior & Janie Bradford.
© Copyright 1959, 1962 Jobete Music Company Incorporated, USA.
Dominion Music Limited, 127 Charing Cross Road, London WC2.
All Rights Reserved. International Copyright Secured.

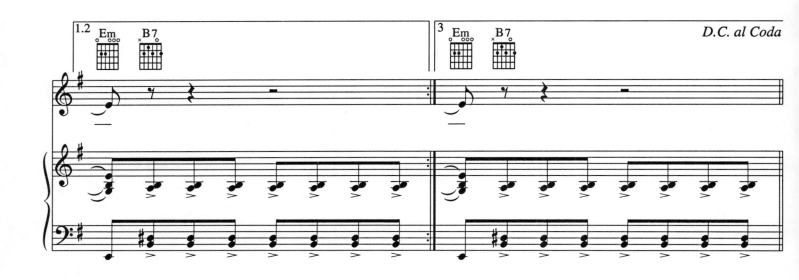

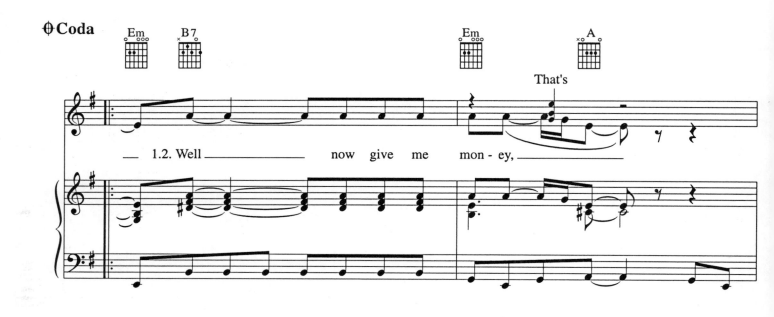

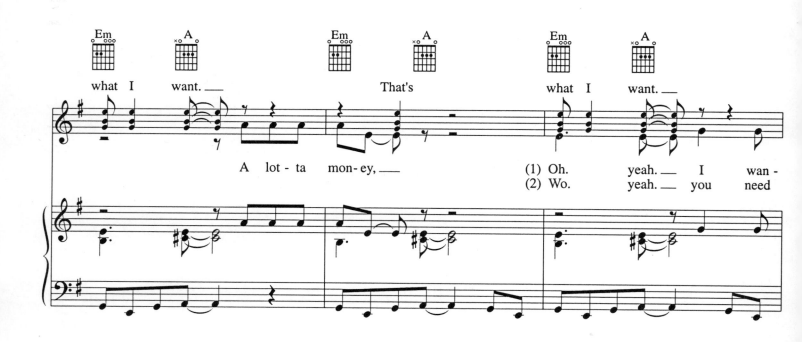

The Beatles

Enya

Phil Collins

Van Morrison

Bob Dylan

Sting

Paul Simon

Tracy Chapman

Eric Clapton

Pink Floyd

New Kids On The Block

Bryan Adams

Tina Turner

Elton John

Bee Gees

Whitney Houston
AC/DC

Bringing you the words

All the latest in rock and pop. Plus the brightest and best in West End show scores. Music books for every instrument under the sun. And exciting new teach-yourself ideas like "Let's Play Keyboard" - in cassette/book packs, or on video. Available from all good music shops.

and music

Music Sales' complete catalogue lists thousands of titles and is available free from your local music shop, or direct from Music Sales Limited. Please send a cheque or postal order for £1.50 (for postage) to:

Music Sales Limited
Newmarket Road,
Bury St Edmunds,
Suffolk IP33 3YB

Buddy

Five Guys Named Moe

Les Misérables

West Side Story

Phantom Of The Opera
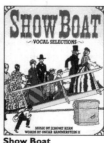
Show Boat

The Rocky Horror Show

Bringing you the world's best music.